CW00541975

I'd like to thank all those that have helped me complete this book in providing their own experiences of mental health.

I'd like to directly thank my family, my partner and his family for always looking out for me and inspiring me.

I'd lastly also like to thank my physio and the NHS mental health teams that have supported me over the years.

Table of Contents

Colour Your Way Through DBT Brought to You by Geonimals

Did you know that one in four people will have experienced some sort of mental health problem or illness in their life?

These illnesses can include depression, anxiety, OCD (Obsessive Compulsive Disorder), PTSD (Post Traumatic Stress

Disorder), BPD (Borderline Personality disorder), Bipolar, psychotic disorders such as schizophrenia or schizoaffective disorder, and eating disorders such as anorexia and bulimia.

Did you know that in the UK there are 1.5 million people who are recorded as having a learning disability?

These disabilities can include ADHD, Dyslexia, Dyspraxia and those on the autistic spectrum.

These problems do not discriminate, so anyone can develop or get a learning difficulty or mental health problem.

The aim of DBT is to help you: understand and accept your difficult feelings, learn skills to manage them and become able to make positive changes in your life.

In this book, we will look at the four main sections of DBT, and these are Mindfulness, Emotional Regulation, Distress Tolerance and Interpersonal Effectiveness.

Each area comes with different skills to try and learn, some of which will be outlined in this book.

Purpose of This Book

This book primarily covers skills for mental health problems through DBT, but I will also cover skills and techniques for learning difficulties from dyslexia to dyspraxia, ADHD and those on the Autistic Spectrum.

This book has three aspects to it, DBT skills for mental health, skills for learning difficulties and colouring too so you are not reading everything all at once, and you can separate it into segments.

What is DBT? – DBT is short for Dialectical Behavioural Therapy.

The word dialectical in DBT does not describe dialect but actually that people can have different ideas that can be true at the same time, so in DBT there are multiple ways to think about a situation, and that all people have something individual to offer, to each situation.

So as an example, you can use multiple techniques to tackle one thought, emotion or cause of distress. Some of these techniques I have outlined in the book may work better for you than others and it is about finding which one works best for you.

Emotions

Emotions are very important as they play an important role in the way we think and behave. In the 20th century, Paul Ekman identified six basic emotions (anger, disgust, fear, happiness, sadness, and surprise) and Robert Plutchik eight, which are shown in the image on the right. The image on the right also shows the complex emotions that come with the basic primary emotions.

The basic emotions are hardwired in us, so even babies display them. Whereas the complex emotions are learnt as you grow.

You experience emotions as a reaction to an event, and sometimes the emotions can last less than a second, and other times they can last weeks, months and even years. For example, depression which comes from the basic emotion of sadness. Depression tends to affect people in the longer term.

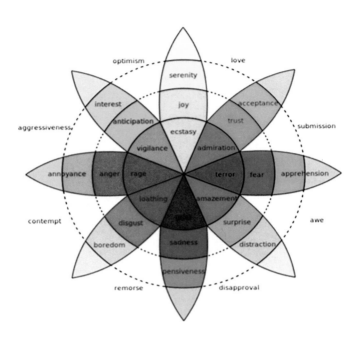

Mindful of Emotion

Being mindful of your emotion involves becoming truly aware of where it has come from. You may want to ask yourself what happened to make you feel that way, it could be something that happened a few days ago or something more recent. And be aware of what thoughts and behaviours have come about from what has happened. Below is a diagram of something you can do if you are unsure of the way you feel and where it came from. So your current thought could be I am so annoyed, which could be anger, and that could lead to you noticing you are clenching your fists, which might have an action of punching the wall, which would lead to some more thoughts and emotions, till you have got to the bottom of what made you angry.

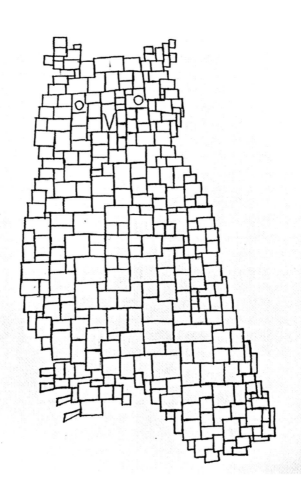

States of Mind

There are three primary states of mind. The rational mind, the emotional mind and between the two you have the wise mind, as shown in the image aside.

As an example, if you have an argument with a friend, and they were behaving not like they would normally do.

With the emotional mind, you might react badly getting angry and the argument will get worse and your friendship may end. Emotional minded people tend to be more hot-headed and impulsive.

The rational mind would try to work out what happened and why your friend was not behaving normally and try to get all the facts. Rational minded people tend to think more logically.

With the wise mind, you would be aware of all the emotions, being aware that you are angry or annoyed, but also try and find out why your friend was behaving strangely, and aware of their emotions, so you can respond appropriately. So, you may ask what was wrong and offer a helping hand.

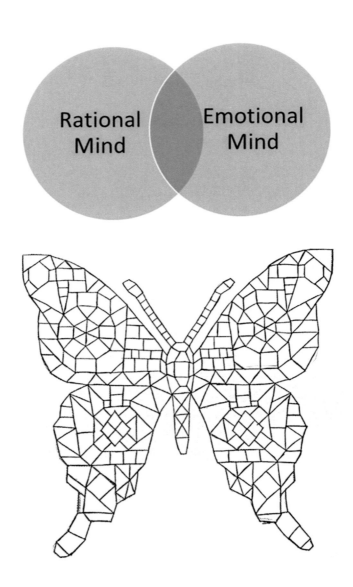

Mindfulness and Grounding

Mindfulness is all about being present in the moment, it draws up on some of the information learnt in the emotions and states of mind pages. You need to acknowledge the thoughts that come in your head and let them pass as being aware of your emotions.

For example, if you are colouring in, which is the purpose of this book, for you to practise your mindfulness by colouring in. When you get a judgemental or intrusive thought come in your head, like a leaf on a river, you need to be aware of it and acknowledge it but then let it pass.

Perhaps you could try colouring in the butterfly on the previous page or the crocodile on the next page, and make a note of what thoughts and emotions come along so you are aware of them, but then you can push them away.

Grounding is another method in the family of mindfulness but is more about being aware of where you are physically so that you can then ground yourself mentally. Start with describing what you can see, for example if you are outside, what colour the sky is, and where there are shadows, and the colours you see of different objects, or you could get more details and observe a particular thing, so if you are near a fountain, you could look at where the water is flowing out, and what statues and ornaments and decorations are there.

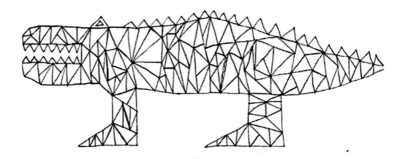

Distress Tolerance - Accepts, Tipp

When you get upset or distressed, sometimes it is hard to come out of the moment or the state you are in to think more rationally and calm yourself down. The techniques in this section are there to help you to calm yourself so that you are then able to think more logically. Even if you are not in a full moment of distress, these techniques may also help prevent distress as well. These techniques are used to try and change the way your body is feeling and your brain is thinking.

Accepts

This is an acronym of a technique known as Wise Mind Accepts. These are all different distraction methods.

A – Activities – Do a different activity, such as read a book, listen to music etc.

C – Contributing – Do something with someone else or for someone else.

C – Comparisons – To compare yourself to others less fortunate than you, such as those in poverty.

E – Emotions – Do something to the opposite emotion you are feeling, if sad, watch something funny.

P – Pushing Away – Push the situation away, try to avoid it till you calm down. T – Thoughts – Distract your mind with counting, like counting 10 orange things in a room, or doing maths.

S – Sensations – Do something to arouse your senses, like holding ice.

TIPP

Another acronym to help you tip the scales of your distress.

T – Temperature – Change your body temperature, if you are hot, have a cold wash or shower.

I – Intense Exercise – Go for a jog or run, do some star jumps to get you to use your pent-up energy and adrenaline.

P – Paced Breathing – Try box breathing, breathe in 4, hold 4, breathe out 4, and hold 4, and repeat, this will calm you down.

P – Progressive Muscle Relaxation – Tighten your muscles and relax them, starting from one end of your body to the other.

Self-Soothe

This technique revolves around all the senses, so touch, smell, taste, sight and sound.

Get some of your favourites of each sense that give you positive experiences and make note of them.

As an example, for me on the sense of smell, what calms me down most or makes me feel less bad is the smell of fresh laundry, or even more so, the smell of the washing tablets. So, when I start to feel distressed, I go to smell some freshly cleaned laundry.

You can do this with all the other senses, so for me what I would pick for taste is a chocolate chip cookie.

I have put a table below for you to fill in, with some examples. What sense?	Sight	Sound	Touch	Smell	Taste
Example	Observe my pet rabbit	Listen to nature sounds	Stroking some really soft wool	Smelling clean laundry	Eating a cookie

Improve the Moment

This is another acronym for a range of things you can try.

I – Imagery – Use your imagination to imagine a positive, happy place, or imagine a new scenario.

M – Meaning – Find meaning to the situation you are in, or a purpose to why you should go beyond the distress.

P – Prayer – This does not necessarily mean pray to god, but you can, or look in towards yourself, to help ground yourself, with mindfulness for example.

R – Relaxation – Do some deep breathing or stretching like yoga, to help relax yourself.

O – One Thing in the Moment – Focus on one thing at a time and use all you brain to focus on that one thing.

V – Vacation – Take a break from what you are doing, see a friend, or just get under the covers of your bed, and just have some time for yourself.

E – Encouragement – Be honest and positive towards yourself. Remind yourself that the emotions or distress you are in at that moment will pass.

These techniques are more effective when used or paired together with another technique such as mindfulness, or even grounding.

Other Methods

Pros and cons – What are the pros and cons to the situation and make a note. For example, pros and cons to binging on some cookies. Pros might be that you will feel better in the moment while you are eating them, but cons could be that it will make you put on weight, or it could even lead to purging.

You must think carefully about all the outcomes, as there may be some unexpected pros or cons, which lead onto each other and could even cause a chain of events.

Ice Diving – This technique is simple but very effective. This is because it switches on the dive response in your brain, which is kind of like switching on a reset button.

Get a big bowl of icy water, take a deep breath in and hold it while you dunk your head in the bowl for 20–30 seconds. After that time has passed take your head out of the water, have a little breather, and repeat 2 or 3 more times.

You may also want to follow this technique up with another for example a distraction.

Half Smile – If you feel a little sad, sometimes tricking the brain is a good technique.

This method is where you put on a very slight smile, not a grin where everyone will notice, but something small enough to make you think you are smiling, which will then trick the brain into thinking you are smiling, and are therefore in a better mood than you thought.

Emotional Regulation

Regulating emotions and trying to control them can be hard. Sometimes in a bad situation we react negatively whether it be anger or fear or even sadness. The skills in this section are to help you to be able to regulate your emotions better, so it will reduce the impact that that situation has/had on you and you will be less vulnerable to those negative emotions.

Please Master

The first skill is an acronym of a few different things to do:

- Treat physical illness,
- Balance eating,
- Avoid mood-altering drugs,
- Balance sleep,
- Get exercise,
- Build mastery.

This is all about looking after yourself physically to then help your mental health.

So, if you are physically ill, prioritise that first, as your health is most important. You then need to assess your eating habits, do you ever binge, purge or restrict eating? Is what you're eating healthy or not?

Avoid taking illegal drugs or even legal highs. You would also want to avoid drinking too much alcohol as that can be a depressant. And the idea is to have your emotions as level as they can be.

Sleep is probably one of the most important ones on this one for me. This is because if I don't sleep enough, I get tired and stressed, and things that would not usually affect me, can sometimes affect me really strongly.

And exercise is also good, as that keeps you fit and healthy, whether you are just going for a walk, or at the gym or going for a run, this will get rid of any pent-up energy and emotions, it also helps with how much you eat and how well you sleep. The last bit is to master all of these parts of PLEASE and then you can start to work more on the harder stuff such as what is causing your emotions to change so drastically.

Positive Experiences

Even when you are in a crisis or feeling bad, there will have been a positive experience of some sort no matter how small it is that would have happened. Whether it be that you had a shower and washed your hair, or even if you went outside, or had a nice cup of tea and chat with someone.

At the end of the day, why not try thinking of your day like a sandwich or a traffic light.

Green – One good thing that happened today e.g. I played with my pet, I had a shower/bath.

Amber – One thing that could have gone better, e.g. I ate half of my sandwich.

Red – One bad thing that happened, e.g. I fell over.

If you want to use the sandwich analogy – one good thing, what could have gone better, and another good thing.

The idea is that over time you will hopefully gain more little good experiences each day, which will total up to be a better day than your originally thought.

For a week, try counting the number of good things, bad things and things that could have gone better that happened on the day.

	Monday	Tuesday	Wednesday	Thursday	Friday	Saturday	Sunday
Green / good things							
Amber / could be better							
Red / bad things							

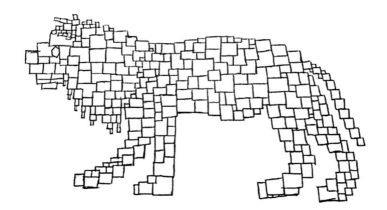

Riding the wave

This is quite simply as it says, riding the wave of all the emotions coming your way. So, if you have an experience that is making you sad just keep going even if you are sad, and the emotion will soon surpass or get easier with time. As time goes by, you become more resilient with the bad things that are happening in your life, so they won't affect you as much.

Opposite Action

This is a good technique when you have done one before it, for example from distress tolerance. The negative behaviour or action that you are about to do, do the opposite.

For example, if I wanted to get a knife, I would get a spoon instead and eat something like a chocolate mousse or whatever was in the fridge.

Or if I wanted to eat something unhealthy, I would do the opposite and make a tea. The act of drinking a nice beverage would make me feel better, and I could use mindfulness when making the tea.

Mindful of emotion

Being mindful of your emotion involves becoming truly aware of where it has come from. You may want to ask yourself what happened to make you feel that way, it could be something that happened a few days ago or something more recent. And be aware of what thoughts and behaviours have come about from what has happened. Below is a diagram of something you can do if you are unsure of the way you feel and where it came from. So you current thought could be I am so annoyed, which could be anger, and that could lead to you noticing you are clenching your fists, which might have an action of punching the wall, which would lead to some more thoughts and emotions, till you have got to the bottom of what made you angry.

Thoughts	Emotions
Behaviours/actions	Bodily sensations

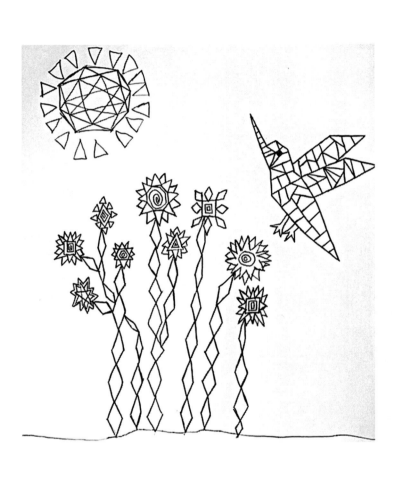

Interpersonal Effectiveness

This module is about how effectively you interact with other people, there are a few different skills you can do to check if you are interacting in an effective way or what you can do better.

Dear Man

This is the first of the techniques:

D – Describe the situation

E – Express your feelings about the situation

A – Ask for what you want

R – Reinforce your willingness to help, and work together on the matter

M – Be Mindful of your goals

A – Appear confident

N – Negotiate.

As an example, if you have just parked your car and someone has blocked you in, rather than get angry and aggressive towards the other person, use this technique. So explain to the person what has happened, that they have blocked you in, and that it annoyed you, and ask for them to move their car just a bit so you can get out. Your goal is to get out of your car, so you can get to work for example, so you have to make sure that you appear confident and work with the other person for them to move their car so you can get out, and lastly you would want to negotiate and compromise a bit so that you both get what you need from the situation. In this case, you both want to get out of your car to get to work. There are always two sides/parties in one relationship, so it is about balancing the needs of both you and the other person.

Give and Fast

G – Be Gentle in your approach

I – Be Interested, listen, don't interrupt

V – Validate

E – Easy manner, use a little humour if possible, don't be too intense.

For keeping relationships healthy you may want to use the GIVE technique, if you are having an argument and you remain calm, listen to what the other person has to say, and validate their reasons or thoughts on what they are saying. Lastly, you may want to use a bit of humour or do something to try and cheer the other person up.

F – Be fair to yourself and the other person

A – (No) Apologies for making a request, saying no or disagreeing

S – Stick to your own values

T – Be truthful, don't lie or exaggerate.

For keeping self-respect you need to remind yourself to remain fair, and remember it's OK to ask for help or to say no if there is something you do not want to do, you don't have to apologise for everything in your life, even if you are saying no to a piece of cake for example. Being truthful and sticking to your values is also important, as if you lie and someone finds out, you will lose their respect and trust, and if you are going through a tough time, and you lie, the person who you lied to, is less likely to trust you and you are more likely to have some of your freedoms taken away.

Activities to Distract You

Do some gardening

Go for a walk, in nature

Watch a movie or TV

Listen to your favourite music

Do some knitting or crocheting

Do colouring, pick a page from this book

Exercise – cycle, go to the gym, go for a run, do some martial arts e.g. Karate or Tai Chi

Help someone

Spend time with family or friends

Play some video games

Dancing

Do some writing in a diary or journal

Practise breathing techniques or meditation

Get your nails done

Go to a spa and treat yourself

Eat your favourite foods

Do some cooking or baking

Watch funny videos on YouTube like cute puppies

Stroke your pet if you have one or go to the local cats and dogs' home.

Sit by the fire, or light a candle

Build Lego or other model building

Play board or card games

Enrol in a class or learn something new

Visit a museum or gallery

Dye your hair or get your hair done

Do or solve some puzzles

Make some food for a meal

Go shopping

Do yoga or Pilates

Start a collection

Clear out your house/room

Go to a car boot sale or round charity shops

Donate to charity

Book something for a future date, like a concert/gig, or even a sky dive!

Call someone in your support network

Inspirational Quotes

The real act of discovery consists not in finding new lands but in seeing with new eyes. – Proust

Life isn't about waiting for the storm to pass. It's about learning how to dance in the rain. – Vivian Greene

Scars remind us where we've been, they do not have to dictate where we are going. – Joe Mantegna

What we do for ourselves dies with us. What we do for others and the world remains and is immortal. – Albert Pine

Do or do not – there is no try. – Yoda

Find the places inside where there's joy, and the joy will burn out the pain. – Joseph Campbell

Out of suffering have emerged the strongest souls, the most massive characters are seared with scars. – Khalil Gibran

Imagination is more important than knowledge. Knowledge is limited. Imagination encircles the world. – Albert Einstein

God grant me the serenity to accept the things I cannot change, the courage to change the things I can and the wisdom to know the difference. – Reinhold Niebuhr

Things in life are never black or white…there are many shades in between, so begore you make a snap judgement consider what's going on around…everyone is fighting some battle of their own. – Karen Kastyla.

Lass alle fünfe gerade sein – German translated into English means let something pass or even more literal let 5 degrees be as they are. So sometimes if it's not perfect, that is also fine.

Everything will be OK in the end. Even if it's not OK, it's not the end. – John Lennon

It does not matter how slowly you go as long as you do not stop. – Confucius

Be miserable. Or motivate yourself. Whatever has to be done, it's always your choice. – Wayne Dyer

Never, never, never give up. – Winston Churchill.

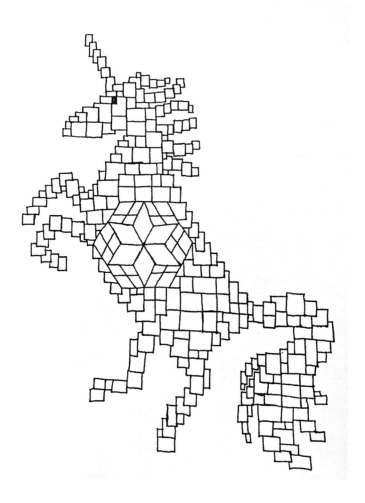

Learning Difficulties

There are many learning difficulties, some of which are listed below, and I have put some techniques which people can use if you have one of them. The first I shall touch on is dyslexia.

Dyslexia

Dyslexia is a learning difficulty which affects reading and writing.

Did you know that Albert Einstein had dyslexia?

The most important thing is to stay calm, and talk to them in a calm manner, so that if people do get irritable, then they are more likely to stay calm.

The best thing to do for dyslexic children is to make learning fun. So, play some games when they are learning, so that you are encompassing, both kinaesthetic, visual and aural types of learning, which will help them learn easier.

Break down the learning into little chunks, and have lots of breaks, as it can get tiring, try to work out the words and then remember the information. Keep things simple as well. This can be done for both adults and children.

Another good way to help learn is to use technology to help people overcome the challenges involved in the situation they are in when it comes to reading and writing. And they can use the muscle memory to type more accurately. As well as most machines having an auto correct.

Don't forget you can also get creative, use music or artwork to help teach.

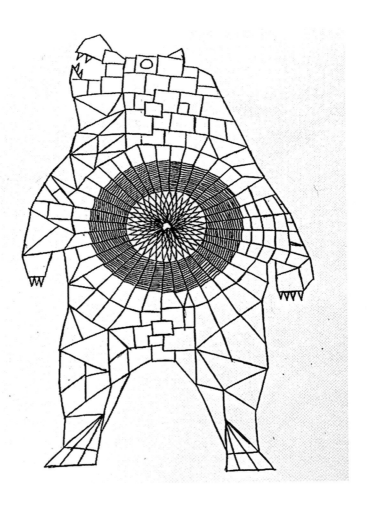

Dyspraxia

Dyspraxia is also known as Developmental Coordination Disorder (DCD).

It is a condition that affects fine and/or gross motor coordination in children and adults. Gross motor coordination skills are important for walking, and posture and other primary movements such as sitting and balancing. Fine motor skills are involved with writing and picking up objects, for example.

Dyspraxia also often causes language problems and people tend not to perceive things correctly, but that is not to say that people with dyspraxia aren't/can't be intelligent.

People with dyspraxia tend to be poorly organised and may not have a good attention span, so children tend to do a lot of foot tapping, or clapping hands, and they are also very fidgety as they struggle to sit still.

To help, you could make the tasks that are needed to be done short and fun.

To help children and adults with coordination skills, maybe take up swimming, horse riding or martial arts.

You have to find a level of learning that is just right, too easy and they will get bored, and work too hard, they will just give up. If they start to get confrontational, then you have to stop, as they may be tired or not in the mood.

If the person has dyspraxia in the workplace, then you will have to allow for reasonable adjustments, so that that person can work as best as they can without any problems. Whether it be that they work in a quieter part of the office for example, or if they work from home, as they tend to work better at home as there are less distractions.

ADHD

ADHD is known as Attention Deficit/Hyperactivity Disorder. People with ADHD often have difficulty paying attention or are hyperactive and impulsive which tends to get in the way of daily functioning and development.

Children with ADHD can be classed as being naughty because they tend not to think of the consequences before they do something that is not appropriate or could be wrong.

As people with ADHD tend not to have good attention spans, keep instructions short and simple and give instructions out one at a time. Give them plenty of praise when they do things well, as positivity often runs onto them with good results.

If you are teaching difficult things, it is best to teach them earlier in the day and leave the easier and more fun materials towards the end of the day. Use visuals as well.

When it comes to tests, do it in a way that works for them, that will still test their knowledge, so orally for example.

Have reasonable adjustments readily available, so separating the work into smaller parts. And if things come in late but are still correct, give them praise, because at least they tried.

You could also use aids to concentrate if it is bad such as medication.

You can also try therapies for ADHD as well to help them with their behaviours and daily thoughts as well as teaching them coping strategies. Some include:

Approaching life like a marathon, so slow and steady wins the race. Make a note of your strengths and allow people to help you with things you are not so good at. Make sure you prioritise your sleep because it can be quite tiring living with ADHD. Having good structure and getting things organised is also key to living more easily with your ADHD.

As with all learning difficulties, it is OK to say no if you know that something will be hard, and it is OK to ask.

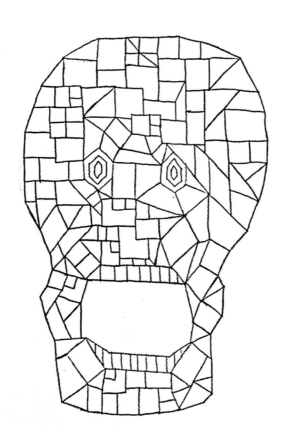

Autistic Spectrum Disorders

Those on the Autistic Spectrum or who have ASD can have varying levels of difficulties.

There are three main areas of difficulty, social interaction, communication and imagination. This means that those with ASD find it hard to understand what others are feeling, struggle with verbal and non-verbal language and find it hard to imagine what others are thinking or thinking outside of their routine.

There also tends to be sensory over and under stimulation, so for example, if you are in a shop and you are sensitive to sounds and sight, it can lead to anxiety and meltdowns because the brain does not know how to process all the information that is coming at it.

So if someone is sensitive to sound, it might be worth buying some ear defenders (look like headphones) to reduce the level of sound that the person hears, so they are less likely to get anxious, or maybe put on some sunglasses in order to block out the bright lights.

You will want to create a structure or routine, that is the same or similar each day or week, so that there are no meltdowns, and so you know what to expect.

Whatever you may want to change outside of the routine has to be done in little steps. Which may take longer, but keep that in mind, so you can time by when it needs to be implemented.

Also, when it comes to food, some people will only eat certain foods, or certain colours, and may avoid some foods due to the texture. So, if for example you wanted to add some more fruit into their diet, that they do not normally have, don't make them eat it right away. If we use a grape, first let them look at it, smell it, or even cut it in half, so they can see the inside and get used to the texture, and maybe even lick it, and get to a point where they are comfortable with the food, so that they will then eat it without too much of a problem. That is not to say that this method works for everyone, some people are more willing to try new things without much of a problem.

Another thing to try when it comes to bedtime and comfort is a weighted blanket, so if it is hot, and you cannot sleep without any form of cover, get a weighted blanket, they can really help calm people down and help you sleep, or put a night light on, for example.

It's all about making people/the person feel as comfortable as possible so that they can continue with their day without many problems or meltdowns.

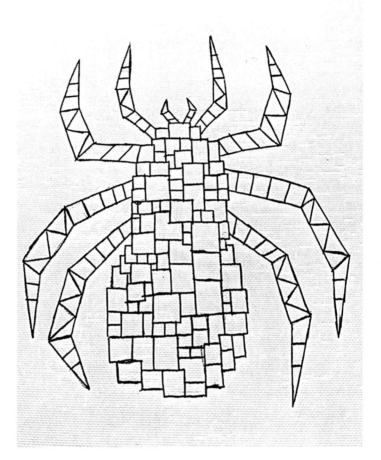

Other Things to Try

Make a crisis plan – you may want someone's help with this one. Think of the different stages that happen when you are going into a crisis – for example:

Stage 1 – Want to be alone and isolate from others, or notice low mood – once you notice that you're in stage one, put in some of the methods outlined in this book, or do some distracting activities.

Stage 2 – Things are starting to get worse, so maybe think about taking any PRN (as and when you need) medication so that if you get to stage 3 you then take it. The aim is to stop you reaching your full crisis point, or at least delay the amount of time till you get there.

If you are having strong urges to self-harm, maybe try holding ice cubes maybe with red dye in them. Or ping rubber bands on your wrists or arms. You could also just draw on your arm or wherever on your body with red pen. You could also perhaps find an activity that gives you as much stimulation as self-harming but not actually hurt yourself or do it safely.

You also need to make sure that you get enough sleep and have a good sleep routine.

Eat well but do allow yourself a treat occasionally. Try and brush your teeth and hair, and have a wash, shower or bath.

Even if you are having a rough time, if you manage to have a wash when you thought you could not, celebrate that. As it's the small victories that will help you get through the day. And when you have got through to the end of the day without self-harming for example, that is also another thing to celebrate, even when you had super strong urges.

Physical health and Mental health

Both your physical health and mental health are linked to one another, from your physical wellbeing and how active you are to what you eat and what other physical health problems you may have.

Nutrition and mental health – based on research it is said that the gut and the brain have a direct connection to each other through signals being sent via the vagus nerve. Your gut creates dopamine and serotonin for example, these neurotransmitters are sent up to the brain affecting mood, memory, appetite, and pain sensations. The brain also sends instructions/communication down to the gut, as it regulates digestion and motility. So the brain tells the gut when to digest and move the waste through your digestive tract.

Imbalances in what you eat affect the gut which can then alter brain function producing inflammation and dysregulating gut-brain communication. Suggesting you may be able to improve your mental health by improving your gut health.

So be aware of what you eat and be aware of what foods make you feel certain ways, as some food can send bad signals to your brain whereas other send good signals. Food can become information to your brain. It is the ones that are good for you that you want to keep eating.

Eating a diverse diet rich in fibre can lead to better mental health. Some people say, try eating the alphabet over a month, you can make a list of plant-based foods, and so long as you eat each letter or as many as you can the better your gut and in turn your brain will feel.

For example, you could include apples, bananas, chickpeas, dill, edamame beans, fennel and so on. Think of as many plant based foods as you can in the alphabet and make a list.

Activity

Research tells us that if you do some form of exercise each day you will feel better.

However, it all depends on your ability to exercise. If for example like me you have fibromyalgia, then it can be very hard to be as active as other people. So, it all depends on what you are able to do.

Some people will notice a difference after they have done a five to ten-minute walk on a day, whereas others may be able to do longer or shorter. Physical exercise is said to be able to reduce stress, anxiety and depression.

But the question leads to, what if I physically can not go outside to walk, due to anxiety or physical inability?

The answer I would say leads to; do whatever you are comfortable with doing. You can do some exercises in your home or even bedroom if you are really struggling. These could range from doing star jumps and dancing to music, to basic arm or leg exercises based on what you are able to do.

If your struggling and can't think of what you can do from home, there are good home workout videos online or you can join a Pilates or yoga class which you can do online.

If you do feel more able you could take up a martial art, or try some other classes like Zumba, or just go to the gym and do what you can.

If you are not able to do anything, don't worry, it's not the end of the world. You can always try again another day when you feel a bit better.

What is it like to live with?

This section is all about mental health illnesses/problems and how people can be affected by them. I have separated the different mental health illnesses however do bear in mind that some people may have multiple illnesses so they could have PTSD and Anxiety so there would be a cross over in symptoms and experiences. No one person is the same, as these illnesses tend to be on a scale one might say, so you can be diagnosed with the same thing but have completely different symptoms.

Things people do not like to hear or see:

- It's all in your head
- Assuming you are dangerous
- Being treated differently
- Get over it, it's in the past
- I understand
- Are you ok?
- You will feel better if you do…
- Just do it, it's not that hard
- Don't be such a wuss
- Pull yourself together
- Judging – never do it, you don't know what it's like.

Things to remember:

- It's not a death sentence, you can still achieve all the things that you want to achieve.
- Take it by hour if the day is too hard, and if that is still too hard take it by minute.
- Sometimes therapy won't work now, so just do your best, keep on fighting.
- So long as you appreciate the little things in life as well, you will find a way, for example being able to have had a bath or shower that day.
- You are not alone.

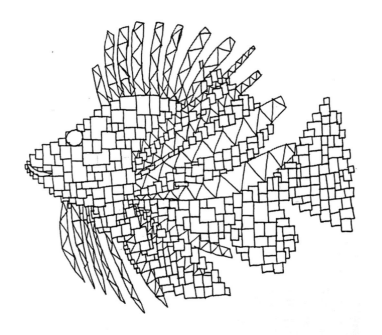

Anxiety

There are many different forms of anxiety ranging from generalised anxiety disorder, to social anxiety and phobias. Phobias can be described as anxiety in its worst form.

There are so many different symptoms of anxiety, and many people experience it very differently.

Most people think that anxiety is defined by panic attacks, but it is a lot more complicated than that. Yes, you can get panic attacks, but living with anxiety can be an ordeal. Some people catastrophise (think the worst is going to happen) which can escalate to a panic attack.

There are times where you in yourself just know you cannot do something as inside you can feel the anxiety creeping in. So sometimes say you were going to go out and meet a friend, you have managed to get dressed but then when you get to the door – bam – you can't, everything stops, and you can't move, and you have to go back in, and cancel as no matter how much you may have wanted to meet up with your friend the anxiety has once again stopped you.

Panic attacks can last from a couple of minutes to hours, and sometimes the effect of one can have you for a few days after. You can get nauseous, or even sick, short of breath, sweaty, increased heart rate and much more. Agoraphobia is a common phobia; it is a fear of going outside or into open spaces. You simply are unable to bring yourself to go outside, and of course the longer you don't go outside, sometimes the harder it is to go outside. Other times people may say to you if you get up and get dressed and we are with you, then you will feel better, but no matter what they say, you don't feel better, and put simply, they just don't understand what it is like to be that afraid of going outside.

Bettina

When I was about 22 years old, I started having panic attacks in public places. I was suffering from accelerated heartbeat, breathlessness, feeling as if the world was caving in on me, and had the strong urge to run away and hide. I was at university at the time, and these attacks made it virtually impossible for me to attend lectures. Even shopping for daily necessities became a struggle, I was only able to shop in small self-service shops, any supermarkets would be too panic inducing. I couldn't make friends as the panic would overwhelm me when trying to communicate with people. On top of that I thought everybody was able to see what was going on inside me. These attacks also overwhelmed me at any time during the day when I was on my own. Therefore, I stayed mostly in my room, gathering strength for the one small shopping trip or the one lecture I had planned to attend that day.

There were several things that helped me overcome this. Firstly, I started running. Whenever a panic attack came and the situation allowed it, I went out and ran. The physical exertion reduces the adrenalin and cortisol levels in the body which drive the panic mode; I was just exhausted afterwards, but at least the panic symptoms were gone for a while. Secondly, I learnt to accept and acknowledge my feelings; it's o.k. to be afraid of certain situations, like going into a room full of strangers you're supposed to communicate with, e. g. at a seminar or workshop.

A piece of good advice was when going the first time to such a place, just to go and observe, without putting myself under the pressure to talk to anybody. And, if worst came to worst, I could always leave the event. This removed some of the pressure to 'perform'. This tactic helped me to 'endure' more and more such situations. It is very important to keep practising subjecting yourself to these uncomfortable situations, as little by little progress is made. Thirdly, I learnt that I don't need to be afraid of the panic attacks. They were disagreeable, but they didn't harm me. When they occurred, I found that, apart from running, deep breathing helped. Furthermore, it is important to realise that you're not alone. Many people experience episodes of anxiety in their lives. It is helpful to talk to understanding family members or friends about it. Finally, counselling by a qualified psychological practitioner is a good way forward if the anxiety is caused by childhood trauma or linked to other psychological difficulties.

Things that I also learnt were not to be too hard on yourself, not to try everything at once, and to avoid unhelpful people. Be kind to yourself and give yourself space and time. Keep practising dealing with uncomfortable situations step by step, at a pace that suits you.

Jordan

I can say that when it comes to mental health issues, for me it is more about feelings, thoughts and patterns around Social Anxiety, Social disconnection, Self-acceptance.

What has helped is: reading, listening to podcasts about psychology, being more open about the issues I was facing/still face, going to the root of those issues (i.e. if having relationship issues, is it me being insecure about something my partner had done, can I reshape the problem into other terms), identifying triggers (i.e. if I'm in a certain situation and my heart starts to race because all these mind questions appear), what is causing this at this precise moment, can I reframe it, take deep breaths, close my eyes, wait a couple of minutes. Further to this, the importance of physical activity and healthy food, this helped phrase the thought and ground it into my mind that taking care of myself was showing me that I cared about me and by replication that moving forward is what I valued.

One last thing, while I have never had any counselling, I am fully for this, there is no stigma and there should never be any, talking about it and phrasing the human aspect of Mental Health is by far the most important thing about it, because all that mental health is about, is Connection or Disconnection. Disconnection from you, or from others.

Donna

I had a lot going on as a teenager both in school and home life. I was absolutely miserable, and I'd say now looking back I probably did have poor mental health but it wasn't something that was discussed in my life.

All I can say is: it really will end. It feels like forever and a day going to school every morning for 7 years, 8 hours a day. Once you're out of the school system you enter a world full of much better, brighter things and much nicer people. You're essentially gathering a group of 100 or so students in a year and expecting them to get along. No one is going to get along with everyone in life, less so when you're all randomly selected to spend 7 years or so together!

People who spread rumours about you, who use words to hurt you, they really are expressing their own internal conflicts and pain by projecting it onto others. It took me a very long time to realise this. They're not as tough as they seem and soon enough, they have to enter the real world outside of school too and quite often the bullies are less prepared for it than those who are bullied. I promise it's not a reflection in your as a person but a reflection on then. Don't dismiss other education based on your school experience. I was adamant I wasn't going to university but my parents wanted me to. Uni was so different, much nicer teachers, much nicer people and I made friends and had a good time. Teachers can be bullies too. There's not much you can do here other than raise it formally and hope for the best. I'd advise just be prepared for this and be smart about how you respond. Don't sacrifice your morals or principles. I never got involved in the smoking/drugs etc and I'm very proud I didn't. It doesn't interest me, it never will. But you are likely to get that pressure. Most of the time and I'm talking 99% of people who offer you something like that just say, "okay cool no worries" and leave it. Don't respond or engage in drama. Even if there's words being said about you.

Schizophrenia

Schizophrenia affects the way you think and see the world. It can cause hallucinations of all senses, for example seeing things or hearing things or voices. One would also have delusional thinking so it can be very hard to distinguish what is real and what is not.

For some people it is never knowing who you are. The voices are constantly telling you who you are, and what you need to do in life, so it can be hard trying to associate with people outside, for example at work.

It can also be very confusing, as if you thought something had happened when it had not, then it can be very upsetting. For example, you could have seen someone that was not there and get scared, because you may think that that person is following you.

In my case I thought that aliens were following me and out to get me, and that people were working with them, so I was convinced for some time that I could only go outside if I wore a tin-foil had either under my normal hat or just in general, to protect me from them from stealing my brain waves. I would also see lots of eyes watching me, UFOs looking for me or abducting people and aliens hi-jacking people. You may have thought that was silly, but when you are that unwell, there is nothing that is silly, it is all very serious and it is a big ordeal living with an unstable mind like that.

Can you imagine seeing things that are not there, or hearing things that are not there, unless you have lived it, you cannot.

Lastly not all hallucinations are bad, there are good ones too.

For example, when I was around nine years old, I started to hallucinate. I felt that they were there to protect me, which I knew that, because it was a tough time, and then the hallucinations would appear, and I knew they would keep me safe. I called her the tree queen and her tree elves; I still believe to this day that they were protecting me.

Depression

Depression normally presents as low mood, but not lasting a few days, it can lasts months or even years.

It is not just low mood though, you lose all motivation to do anything, and it feels like an endless empty void. To start with you don't see a way out, all you have is the darkness and endless emptiness, so empty you become unable to have emotions. You no longer experience joy or pleasure.

At this point, you may start wondering if there is any point to living, and suicidal thoughts occur. To start with they are just the odd one here or there, but the longer you are in this place of darkness, in this abyss, the more thoughts, and ideas come to mind.

Thoughts then start to come in, about if there is another way to start to feel something other than this emptiness, you no longer experience positive emotions.

This is where some people try to self-harm, it's a release, to feel something, anything other than this empty nothingness. Some people self-harm as a way of punishing themselves, whereas others may self-harm to feel some form of emotion, whether it's pain or pleasure from the act of self-harming. You feel something so you continue to cut or scratch or pull your hair as an example. Each time you feel so bad and empty, that brief amount of emotion helps just a little bit. However, some people can feel so bad and empty that they feel like they can no longer continue, that it will never get better, so they get lots of intrusive thoughts, suicidal thoughts. Some people act on them and succeed, whereas some people act on them but continue to live.

If they succeed and do take their life, you may think, is there anything else I could have done, why didn't they approach me? The questions are endless. In the end, no matter how much you do or don't understand, the person that did take there life, honestly thought there was no way out, that it was the best for everyone, and that they may have even been a burden.

If they do not succeed, and do continue to live, there is a chance that you can help them find the way out, and reassure them that life is worth living, and though it will take time you will start to feel better again. It will start like a faint candle in an endless empty tunnel, and you can turn to that candle and start to see the way out, no matter how long it takes.

Cora

Symptoms of my depression were not wanting to go out of bed at any time in the day, not wanting to meet people or doing any activity inside and outside the house. Not having the strength to cook any meals and not caring if I was eating or not.

Feeling sad all the time and needing to cry, having the lack of will to live and feeling like there is no solution and I was going to feel that sad forever.

My depression episodes have been related to my mother's health problems. She has suffered from uncommon illnesses plus two strokes which needed intensive care. Taking care of her put a lot of pressure, guilt, and stress on myself, so when she was better that I was able to see it myself, my stress became depression. I am also sensitive to the weather changes and the lack on sun affects my moods. I have Polycystic Ovaries Syndrome and Hypothyroidism, both chronic illnesses which can lead to depression.

What helped was talking therapy and antidepressants. When I got to the darkest mental state, I realised that talking therapy wasn't enough to break the negative cycle in my brain. I have tried three types of antidepressants: one of them caused me an allergic reaction on my skin (Citalopram), another one accelerated me too much (Prozac) and the third one luckily didn't give any side effects (Sertraline).

I got talking therapy for two years and it helped me a lot to identify what things were creating negativity and how to deal with them. I learnt a lot about myself and improved my relationships with family.

I also felt specially judged by some friends and family as 'being weak for taking antidepressants and not being able to get out of depression on my own'. That made me feel even worse, like a loser who could have chosen feeling well but chose to feel sad instead.

Gertrude

So, my symptoms and experience have been related to my depression and anxiety. Low energy, suicidal thoughts, sleep paralysis, communication problems, and an inability to hold a steady job.

I grew up in an environment in which I was constantly moving, I moved to over 10 countries before the age of 11. Forming connections has proved to be extremely difficult for me growing up, and a feeling of being very 'other' left me very disconnected.

Symptoms of depression I had since the age of 11, perhaps earlier. However, I was raised in an environment which I would define now as 'toxic positivity' , songs that I was accustomed to hearing had the lyrics 'Happy all the time'. Expressing negative emotions was considered to be 'Complaining' and dealing with your emotions was a matter of labelling them as very black and white, and ridding yourself of anything negative.

Of course, coming from this environment, I struggled a lot to properly engaging with my emotions. My anxiety was made worse by suppressing what I viewed to be negative, or feel like I was the problem because I shouldn't feel this way or was indulgent or feeling sorry for myself.

The biggest breakthrough for me was understanding the complexities of emotions, ridding myself of the imposed idea that it comes down to willpower or the 'right' attitude'. That feeling negative about something is not always a negative feeling, it can be the step between negative space and taking control to navigate your way to a more positive one. Whether this is medication, behaviour, lifestyle change, or learning and practicing healthy coping techniques.

If I could give advice to anyone that has been recently diagnosed.

Take advantage of the information age, as overwhelming as it can be, is knowledge and such a wide range of practices. That's not to say you should follow someone's opinion or expertise blindly or that there are a bunch of quick fixes on there, but there is a wealth of knowledge and a lot of writings and research that can prove useful in understanding yourself and others better.

Invest in therapy. I used the excuse I cannot afford it for way too long. Whilst at the same time casually spending the same money on escapist activities which only drove me further and further in the wrong direction. Following patterns that felt 'natural' and becoming frustrated by the end result. Forming a deeper understanding of myself and why my experiences have brought about my pattern and the choices I make has helped me in understanding and feeling more empowered to respond in life rather than react. Which is so worth it! Therapy is becoming more and more accessible to and finding the right person for what you are suffering with/ your background is easier than before, you are not confined to your geographical location. The most important relationship you have is with yourself, so invest in it.

Practicing gratitude, I had trouble for a while discerning between what was healthy positivity and toxic positivity, and gratitude has helped me form a more authentic relationship with positivity.

Bipolar

Bipolar shows itself by radical changes in moods, so you can be at rock bottom one day and then you may completely manic/on top of the world the next day.

BPD

Borderline Personality Disorder is described as changing moods, self-image, and behaviour. This can result in impulsive actions, erratic moods, and problems in relationships with other people.

Due to the severe changes in moods and therefore actions people can; feel isolated or abandoned by others, struggle coping with stress and the strong emotions that come with it. This can lead to self-harming and suicidal thoughts and actions as well as misusing alcohol and drugs both legal and illegal. You may also struggle with looking after your home, looking after relationships, and staying in work. BPD is also known as EUPD - Emotionally Unstable Personality Disorder.

OCD

Obsessive Compulsive Disorder is described by the need to do something. There are different types of OCD. These include doing things on a loop, repetitive actions, as a way of creating a safety net, they do what feels safe for them, and this tends to be repetitive, and if something is slightly different it can cause a meltdown.

Behaviours can include counting things, checking food repetitively, listening to the same song repeatedly, washing hands, cleaning multiple times, ordering things and repetitive thoughts.

It is an anxiety related condition, so you can get frequent intrusive thoughts about something, and then you if you want to feel safe you repeat an action or you create certain rituals, for example if you knew something was potentially dangerous due to what you had thought, you would avoid that at all costs to reassure you, so nothing bad will happen.

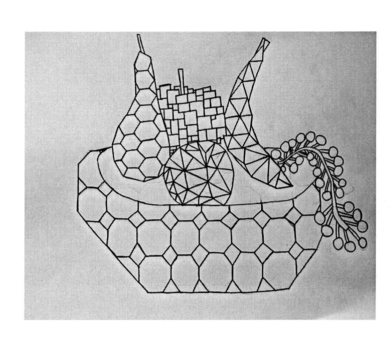

PTSD

Post-Traumatic Stress Disorder is as it says on the box, it is a reaction to trauma that you get after it has happened. You can start to get it, a few months after the trauma has occurred, or a few days after, but it can also start years after the trauma occurred, and it can last for years.

So never ever say, it's in the past, why are you still not over it?

The answer is simple, they relive the event over and over, it can be once a month, every day or even once every few years. No matter how often they relive it, they do. So, in some cases you may never get over it.

PTSD can be triggered in different people in different ways, from getting a flashback to a song, or if someone comes up behind you to talk to you. Flashbacks can happen in any of the senses as all senses are present at the time of the trauma, so it could even be a certain smell that triggers it.

It also makes you very sensitive to certain situations and can bring on anxiety and depression. As if there is something that triggers off a flashback, you may get anxious about being near it, seeing it or listening to it again. So, you can develop anxiety around it.

Not all the flashbacks have to be bad, in my experience, you can have flashbacks of both good and bad memories. Its just the way it is interpreted which makes it good or bad, so to me they are good memories some of them, whereas others say that that should be a bad memory.

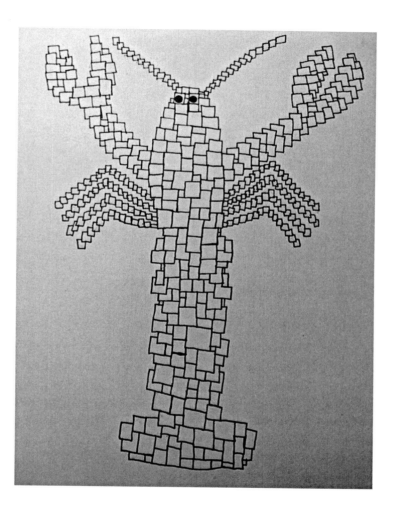

Eating Disorders

Having an eating disorder tends to mean that you have an unhealthy relationship with food. There are many different eating disorders, some common ones include anorexia, bulimia and binge eating disorder.

With anorexia people tend to restrict their eating in such a way that they lose weight. A lot of people with anorexia can also have body dysmorphia, which is when you see yourself in weight that is not. So you could be dangerously thin but still believe that you are overweight.

With bulimia people tend to binge and eat a lot of food, but then they will feel bad for having eaten and then purge. Purging tends to be getting rid of all the food you have eaten, either by forcing yourself to vomit or by taking a lot of laxatives.

With binge-eating disorder people tend just to eat an unhealthy amount of food. Normally people are overweight, and sometimes forget when they last had food, so will eat again.

Geraldine

Anorexia is such an illogical and complex disorder that not even Anorexics know how to explain or understand it fully themselves. It follows no sense or pattern, even when similar traits are shown between people. The easiest way I can describe it, is having control over something so out of control it is physically and mentally painful. I was 12 when my eating disorder started. By 13 years old, I was admitted to the general hospital for IV fluids and tube feeds. My BMI was dangerously low, my blood sugars were classified as fatal, my electrolytes were completely off balance and my heart was very weak. Following a 3 week stay, I was admitted to an adolescent psychiatric unit, and finally left (after 3 short, failed discharges and further general hospital admissions) a week before my 15th birthday. A couple of years after, I wrote some reflections on my disorder based on diary entries. Here is a little insight:

"If you ask me every emotion I felt when I was laid back there, in that hospital bed, I would be able to articulate it with certainty; frustrated, scared, sad, angry. Furious even. But with who? The white bottom sheet was crisp and unslept in, the turquoise blanket for a duvet they offered much too cold. The smell of blood and sweat and clinical product hanging in the air. The beeping noise of the various plugged machines amongst the ward. The red kite and familiar mapping of the county curtains drawn around the bed. One pine single door cabinet beside the bed, and a wheeled tray at just above bed height to the left. Three untouched magazines at the bottom of the bed, next to the patient notes hanging on the bed bar.

And beside me to the right, my sleeping mother, slumped over the bed, her clammy hand grasping mine. Her quiet snores were the only evidence of her life; the way she laid across my legs and her pale, unpeaceful face indicated someone who had no life left in them. I briefly considered it ironic that even though I was at risk of dying, I felt more alive than anyone else looked. Perhaps the adrenaline my body was producing to keep my body warm and my heart beating, perhaps the energy my brain was producing from feeling so powerfully in control, despite the motives being somewhat deceitful. Starve yourself, it said, no one has to know. Cover your tracks and comply, slip it here and there. By the time they realise, it will be too late. You'll already have achieved what you want.

What did I want? I was not led by deep vanity telling me to be beautiful. The beautiful feeling was an incentive, but not the cause. Perhaps to lie to myself and say it was all about beauty would make it easier to overcome, but as the case was, it was simply a block to eat. A fear that ran deeper than vanity and power. This was a loss of control in the most controlled manner, like being at the knees of your own self. There was no temporary way of crossing the line, no 'it doesn't matter, you can burn it off later.' There was simply no room, no negotiation. Do not eat, do not drink. Even if it kills you."

And that's the ultimate sadness—I didn't mind if it killed me. It was such a natural way for my body and brain to behave, the way my brain worked was so normal to me that I thought other people were mad for not working the same way. Which is interesting, because I was not always like that; yet in the midst of Anorexia, I couldn't remember being any other way.

I was of working class, I had a loving family, but my childhood was somewhat disruptive and difficult, which I won't go into. But like others I knew—there was no final or massive trauma that set it off. It was probably an accumulation of challenges, that eventually switched something on (or off) within me.

A lot of my Anorexic behaviours were very typical— shaking my legs to burn calories, over-exercising, occasional bulimic tendencies, self-harming, starvation, hiding food (at any cost), hiding weights in my underwear and drinking large quantities of water to appear heavier on weigh-ins, mood swings inflicted by being 'forced to eat' and a level of uncompromising personality. Of course, despite it not being the ultimate reason (and in line with common belief), vanity was a part of it too. Not in the sense I wanted to look the best, but in the sense it made me feel my best. Bones on show and low numbers were addictive and rewarding. It felt truly beautiful. I would walk around feeling like I was floating, so unattached to the earth. I loved to see my bruises as a result of those bones sticking out too much. I wore my old clothes like medals as they hung baggy over me. I got jealous of others who I thought were skinnier (and of course, when I looked in the mirror I was always so much fatter). Besides evidence indicating otherwise, I never felt 'skinny'. It was an unachievable goal, because ultimately it was never enough.

Being an inpatient was so difficult, it has changed and shaped me forever as a person. I think this is partially because I was so young and away from home, and partially because I picked up so many unhealthy traits while I was there, both from other patients and the overall (at times) mistreatment. I was away from home for long periods of time, and only allowed to see family if I complied with my diet plans, reached a certain weight/activity level and avoided self-harm or suicidal tendencies (which to start with, was a long time). I was the youngest for a long time too and became very much a little sister to the other patients. They took care of me, but some had very challenging disorders that exhibited unhealthy behaviours (the unit looked after a range of illnesses including schizophrenia, psychosis, bipolar, eating disorders, depression, OCD etc.), and being so young I picked up on these very quickly, and incorporated them into my own illness subconsciously. Alongside this, staff could be cruel and not very understanding of my disorder. I was often forced to eat things that made me sick (for example, I was intolerant to egg, and they did not believe me, so I was forced to eat an egg sandwich that made me violently sick for days), forced to eat things I had never liked in my life, and forced to eat things that weren't normal habits for any person, such as lumps of butter and orange peel. On one occasion, I threw all the cakes in the bin, and a staff member grabbed me by the shoulders, shook me and called me a 'selfish cow'. It's important to remember that there were wonderful people there too, who really went above and beyond to support me—mainly the school team, who were a huge part of my rehabilitation and success in education going forward, as well as a distraction from the troubles I was facing at the time. In my adult life, these experiences do affect me. I get comfortable in being lonely, I struggle to let people in, am very independent (sometimes too much, as I struggle to ask for help), and have never shared my experiences to those currently in my life.

The turning point in my recovery was when I realised, I wanted more. I wanted more for myself, and for those I was hurting around me. I had lost my childhood sweetheart through my actions and had uneasy relationships with my family who I was once so close to. I had one true friend who stuck with me through that time (and we are still friends today), but otherwise I had no friends, very little schooling, and was as unconfident and uncomfortable as I'd ever been. One small action changed my whole thought process. One night on leave from hospital, I made the decision to go into my mum's fridge at home, and by choice eat a slice of cheesecake that secretly I had been craving. This was the first of my actions that I did because I wanted to eat, not because I was being forced to through threats or because it was on my calculated diet plan. And although it wasn't the end of my recovery, it was certainly the beginning.

It has been over 10 years since my eating disorder began to unravel. Since leaving hospital for good, I have found a way to control it, to the point that it doesn't really affect my life anymore. I am a healthy weight, and enjoy eating, both on my own, with friends and family. I have had two healthy children, despite being told that my loss of periods would probably lead to infertility. I am very lucky. However, the road to recovery was not smooth-sailing. I still have bad times where Anorexia pops it's head up and tries to pull me back. It happens in cycles, sometimes months or years apart. The only pattern I have found is that the switch flips if I try to diet of any kind, or if my weight drops below a certain point. For this reason, I have to avoid fasting for long periods of time, dieting for long periods of time, and aim to keep my weight between 8 ½-9 1/12 stone, what I've found to be my 'safe' weight (any less or more and I get 'triggered'). Overall, I am now a fairly healthy (though I will always have a weak heart), well-educated and happy young lady. I live alone with my children in our flat, which has really moulded into our home the last four years, and I take great pleasure in cooking for friends and family, as well as eating with them—something I once could not have stomached the thought of.

What I would tell someone who is just coming to terms with the disorder, is that no matter how little you believe it, there is more outside of Anorexia. Recovering is one of the hardest things I have ever had to do, but it was worth it. If I had given in, I would have certainly died by now, either through health complications or suicide and I'd have missed out on all the beautiful things I have experienced since. Now I take pleasures in the small things, small things I didn't notice or fully enjoy when Anorexia consumed my life, like singing in the car with my friends on hot summer days and ordering a treat takeaway with my children as we snuggle up at night. Things that feel impossible to achieve, start with the decision to want something more. And you are worth it. There is a place in this world for you.

And for anyone who is supporting an Anorexia sufferer, remember that the illness is in the brain, not their weight. Many Anorexics retain their Anorexia thought processes even when they are a 'healthy' weight. You never quite know when their switch has flipped, when they're on the edge of a spiral, or when they're feeling overwhelmed. Try to be patient and understanding. They're not trying to be selfish, or vain. Whether they have suffered for a long time, or it's quite new, they don't want to think or feel this way any more than you want them to. Unconditional love is the only thing that will help them through it.

Jess

Anorexia, bulimia, and everything in between. The thing with eating disorders is that, like most conditions, you never think you will suffer with one. And the other thing about eating disorders—especially those of a restrictive nature—is that they grab hold of your life so slowly and yet so fast, that you don't even notice. There is not one defined cause of eating disorders and there never will be. They are a result of genetics, coupled with some maladaptive thinking and certain environmental factors. It is estimated 1.25 million people in the UK suffer with an eating disorder, however many more never seek medical help or receive a diagnosis. Anorexia carriers the highest mortality rate of any psychiatric illness, with other eating disorders such as bulimia and binge eating disorder also causing severe clinical issues.

My lived experience of an eating disorder

Before we delve into the depths of living with a psychiatric illness, I'll introduce myself. My name is Jess, and I am happy to say I have reached 25 years of age, despite the complications of the previous decade. I am by no means a seasoned writer, but that does not mean I can't tell my story in the hope to make one more person feel less alone with their struggle or to spread some awareness on the subject.

"When did it start?" people often ask. On reflection, there were signs I may have had food issues from as young as 10, however a more definitive point was at 14 years of age. The age of getting boyfriends, taking a more active interest in my own appearance and the pressure of exams looming. I used to eat what I want, when I want and never think about how I looked. I was more interested in climbing trees, cycling round the block, and wrestling my younger brother. Suddenly I was in the whole new world of 'becoming a woman.' I had become aware my body shape was no longer long and narrow, and that there were new softer curves appearing. There were other girls I was jealous of and wanted to be 'petite' like them. (Not understanding I couldn't become 4 inches shorter with a small bone structure).

I began 'eating healthily.' I wasn't permitting myself to eat any sweets, chocolate, and various other things. I started obsessively weighing myself, once, twice, up to eight times a day in the hopes I'd lose another gram. I did begin to lose weight. After a while it became noticeable, and I received compliments of my figure from people who didn't know I was effectively starving myself. However, this reinforced these behaviours. If I could be good at anything, I'd be the best at being thin.

Over time, my body became so starved that I began binge eating. For anyone who doesn't know, binge eating isn't a big splurge or being 'naughty' by overindulging. It's a complete loss of control. It's two portions of Bolognese, seven chocolate bars, a sharing bag of crisps, half a loaf of bread, ten biscuits, three cereal bars, half a tub of ice-cream and more in one sitting, in a short amount of time. To the point of being in agony from the fullness. Unfortunately, my response to this was to be sick. On the worst days, I would binge and purge up to six times a day and then collapse in a dehydrated heap into bed with sore teeth and the acid burning my throat.

I eventually confided in my mother about my behaviours. For anyone who has opened up to someone about their mental health, it is no small feat. I was immediately referred to the child and adolescent mental health services. Throughout various appointments over a few years I managed to stop bingeing and purging, however the restrictive nature of my eating disorder worsened, to the point of being admitted to a psychiatric residential facility. I semi-recovered with the intensive help of various health care professionals over 4 months, however the real recovery I did alone. From the age of 17 to 18 I made a concerted effort to commit to recovery. I reached a point where I knew I could continue letting anorexia rule my existence or choose life. Seven years on, I am pleased to say I no longer suffer with anorexia. I would be lying if I said the thoughts are completely gone, however like most mental illnesses you get better at self-managing and making positive choices.

What should people know about eating disorders?

Eating disorders serve as a coping mechanism to an individual, no matter how damaging they are. This makes them incredibly hard to recover from, as they are almost a best friend, making you feel safe and 'in control.' The real tragedy being that they ultimately completely control you.

There is a lot of shame and embarrassment that comes with having an eating disorder. Food is such an integral part of life, that it is often hard to hide having an eating disorder and occasions based around food can bring great distress. In supporting someone with an eating disorder, one should never comment on the individual's weight or food habits, even if they seem like positive observations. Ask the person if there is anything you can do to make their experience more comfortable, especially in distressing situations.

Mental health awareness if ever increasing (thankfully), however we all play a part in opening these lines of communication with each other to create a network of support and trust.

UK Helplines

Mencap – for learning disabilities - 0808 808 1111 - https://www.mencap.org.uk/

Beat – for eating disorders - Youthline: 0808 801 0711 Helpline: 0808 801 0677 - https://www.beateatingdisorders.org.uk/

Anxiety UK – for anxiety - 03444 775 774 / text 07537416905 - https://www.anxietyuk.org.uk/

CALM (Campaign against living miserably) – for men's mental health- 0800 58 58 58 - https://www.thecalmzone.net/

Mind – for mental health - 0300 123 3393 - https://www.mind.org.uk/

National Autistic Society – for autistic people - 0808 800 4104 - https://www.autism.org.uk/

PAPYRUS (Prevention for young suicide) - 0800 068 4141 - https://www.papyrus-uk.org/

Rethink Mental Illness – for mental health - 0300 5000 927 - https://www.rethink.org/

Samaritans – confidential phone line for all - 116 123 - https://www.samaritans.org/

Samaritans – confidential phone line for all - 116 123 - https://www.samaritans.org/

References

https://www.psychologytoday.com/gb/blog/hide-and-seek/201601/what-are-basic-emotions
https://dialecticalbehaviortherapy.com/
https://www.dbtselfhelp.com/
https://drruscio.com/best-diet-for-brain-health/
The Stress Solution- 2018 - Dr Rangan Chatterjee
https://www.nimh.nih.gov/health/publications/borderline-personality-disorder/index.shtml

Hi! my name is Lorna and I have written this book because what's in here has helped me and I hope it will help you too.

I have Asperger's (on the autistic spectrum) and I have also lived with and currently live with depression, anxiety, schizoaffective disorder and PTSD for a lot of my life. I developed these conditions as a result of some situations I had in my life. In 2013, when I was 17, I was admitted to psychiatric hospitals, and that is where I properly started to get help, and where I was first properly diagnosed with Asperger's.

I found that talking therapies to start with did not help so much, for example CBT and just talking, because when I was in the moment of distress, I simply could not talk about it. This is when DBT (Dialectical Behavioural Therapy) was offered to me. This really helped, as it helped me deal with my emotions there and then so that I could settle and calm down, to then talk about the issues that were causing the distress.

Once I had a variety of different skills in my arsenal, that I could apply to many situations, and when I could also link the skills to take me to a calmer place, that was only then when the trauma work, talking therapies and CBT could really take effect.

I also found that there are a lot of self-help books out there based on CBT, but nothing for learning a skill to help you in the moment, so I have amalgamated all that I have learnt with DBT and other skills for learning difficulties and put it into this book.